20th century icons
DESIGN

ISBN 1 899791 82 5
First published in 1999 by Absolute Press,
Scarborough House, 29 James Street West,
Bath, Somerset, BA1 2BT, England
T 01225 316013 **F** 01225 445836
E info@absolutepress.demon.co.uk

Icons selected by James Dyson
Text by Andrew Langley
Series Editor: Camilla Ford
Design: Christine Leech

Printed by Phase Print Ltd, Underwood, England

20th century icons
DESIGN
selected by James Dyson

Acknowledgments

Thanks are due to all of the individuals, companies and organisations who helped towards the production of this book. Many provided material and information that was greatly appreciated. In particular, Absolute Press and Terrence Higgins Trust would like to thank the following for their generous commitment to the project.

Arcaid
The Factory
2 Acre Road
Kingston-upon-Thames
Surrey KT2 6EF
T +44 (0) 181 546 4352
F +44 (0) 181 541 5230
E arcaid@arcaid.co.uk
W http://www.arcaid.co.uk

Aviation Photographs International
15 Downs View Road
Swindon
Wiltshire SN3 1NS
T +44 (0) 1793 497 179
F +44 (0) 1793 434 030

Hulton Getty Picture Collection
Unique House
21-31 Woodfield Road
London W9 2BA
T +44 (0) 171 266 2662
F +44 (0) 171 266 3154
E info@getty-images.com
W www.hultongetty.com

Martyn Goddard
T +44 (0) 207 485 7568
F +44 (0) 207 485 0996
E photomg@compuserve.com

Contents

All royalties from the sale of this book, plus a matching donation from the publisher will benefit the Terrence Higgins Trust, the UK's leading HIV and AIDS Charity.

(registered charity no. 288527).

Terrence Higgins Trust

I'd like to extend my personal thanks on behalf of the Terrence Higgins Trust to everybody involved in the *20th Century Icons* series of books, particularly James Dyson who has devoted not only his talent, time and effort into producing this wonderful book but has also agreed to donate his royalties to the Terrence Higgins Trust. This generosity has been matched by Absolute Press who will be making a donation to equal the royalties.

I have been involved personally in the fight against HIV and AIDS since the disease first appeared in the UK in 1982 and the Terrence Higgins Trust was founded. Our work to stop the spread of HIV and support people living with and affected by HIV and AIDS is as important now as it was then.

Last year a record number of people were diagnosed as having HIV and the Terrence Higgins Trust provided services to over 11,000 people – many of them living not only with this terrible disease, but also facing discrimination and poverty. It is thanks to the generosity of James Dyson, everybody else involved in the preparation of this book and the concern of people like you that the Terrence Higgins Trust is able to undertake its vital work.

Nick Partridge OBE
Chief Executive

‘For me, design is about how something works, not how it looks. It's what's inside that counts.’

James Dyson

James Dyson

James Dyson was born in 1947 and educated at Gresham's School in Norfolk, the Byam Shaw School of Drawing and Painting and the Royal College of Art (both in London). At the Royal College he trained as a product designer, gaining several commissions while still a student.

In 1970 he joined the Bath-based engineering firm of Rotork, managing the Marine Division. Four years later, he struck out on his own to develop the revolutionary Ballbarrow, for which he won a Building Design Innovation Award.

He sold his shares in the Ballbarrow in 1978 to fund a new venture – the bagless vacuum cleaner. Over the next five years he built over 5,000 prototypes, before launching the G-Force in 1983. The huge success of this paved the way for the Dyson DC01, which appeared in 1993. It was soon the best-selling vacuum cleaner in the UK, and is now exported around the world. James Dyson was awarded the CBE in 1998.

Foreword

'By having good designs, you have workmen who work, not merely with their hands, but with their hearts and heads too; otherwise you will merely get the fool or the loafer to work for you.'

Oscar Wilde

It seems to me that most of the time, people don't consider how the objects that surround them in their everyday lives came into existence. Most people only consider how something was designed if it doesn't work, then they kick and demand to know 'who designed this?' The best and most creative products evolve as part of a design process, in which the technology on the inside informs the way that they look on the outside. The success of British companies such as JCB and Rolls-Royce Aerospace illustrate the importance of keeping technology and innovation at the heart of design. For the same reason, the Citroën DS, with its many technological patents, innovative suspension system and inimitable shape still stands comparison with cars designed today.

For me, design is about how something works, not how it looks. It's what's inside that counts. The best designs are the result of someone questioning everything around them – looking at the same things as everyone else but thinking something different.

James Dyson

Berenice Lamp

1985 Paolo Rizzatto and Alberto Meda

Wherever you go, the Berenice lamp will follow. The two concentric rings allow for the head to be grasped and rotated through 360°.

Rizzatto was already a celebrated designer when he founded his own company for manufacturing lamps in Milan in 1978. The resulting Luceplan products conveyed much of his humour and technical imagination to a wider market, and emphasised his conviction that lamps are capable of creating a unique and inspiring atmosphere.

The Berenice lamp is, in essence, a simple angle-poise light for the table, made of metal and glass. Yet Rizzatto and Meda transformed this basic shape into a supremely elegant object. Its long fishing rod stem and angled arm seemed to defy gravity, but the weighty base enabled it to stand firm in any position.

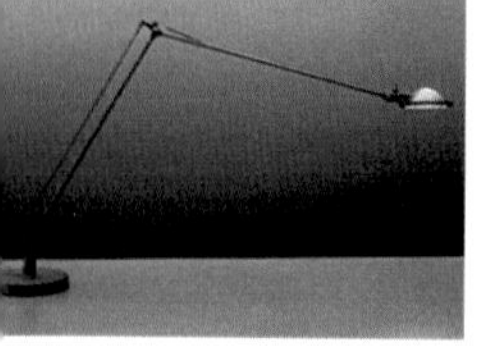

The Berenice family has produced many siblings. The current range includes variations to mount on the wall or stand on the floor – various colours and sizes to boot.

Concorde

1969 BAC/Sud

The Soviet answer to the Concorde – the ill-fated Tupolev Tu 144 – was dubbed 'Concordski' by the ever imaginative British press.

Fuel is pumped from one part of Concorde to another to maintain the aircraft's flight balance as the tanks empty.

British prestige suffered plenty of blows during the early 1960s. Among them was the abrupt cancelling of the entire programme for developing supersonic combat aircraft. One allied project did go ahead, however – and was to inject a big dose of pride into the national psyche.

The BAC/Sud Concorde was revolutionary in many ways. It carried commercial passengers at speeds much faster than sound (up to Mach 2, in fact). It boasted a stunningly beautiful double-delta wing formation with no need for a tail. And – perhaps most amazing of all – it was developed simultaneously in two sites, Toulouse in France and Filton in the UK.

Both prototypes embarked upon their maiden flights on the same day in 1969, provoking much public euphoria. Concorde's commercial success was to be limited by high running costs, but its slender, elegant shape (accompanied by the harsh roar of its afterburners) soon became a familiar and enchanting sight in British skies.

Hovercraft

1959 Christopher Cockerell

In Canada, specially adapted hovercraft are used to break ice on waterways.

The main obstacle to speedy travel – on water or land – is drag. One neat answer to this problem of friction, first researched in the 1870s, was to float the vessel concerned on a cushion of compressed air. Thus, it does not touch the water, but hovers above it.

A hovercraft can be steered by rudders, propellers or small doors in the skirt called 'puff ports'.

Hovercraft can't go up-hill.

No practical breakthrough came, however, until the 1950s, when the British scientist Christopher Cockerell devised the first successful Air Cushion Vehicle or 'hovercraft'. His SRN-1 created a sensation when it was launched in 1959. Gas turbine engines powered the lift fans, which sucked in air and forced it down into a space beneath the vessel. This air cushion was contained within a flexible rubberised skirt.

Driven forward by aircraft propellers, the hovercraft was highly manoeuvrable and could reach speeds of over 100 km/h (62 mph). A larger model, capable of carrying over 400 passengers and 60 vehicles, soon established itself as an alternative (and less nauseating) ferry across the English Channel.

hovercraft

The Princess

Citroën DS

1955 Citroën

The Citroën DS needed no conventional jack when a wheel had to be changed. The pneumatic suspension did the job.

One unfortunate side-effect of the DS's rolling suspension for many passengers was a kind of sea-sickness.

The launch of the Citroën DS19 staggered the motoring world in 1955. It was, simply, the most technically advanced saloon car ever seen. To enhance the effect, Citroën christened it the 'Goddess' or 'Déesse' – hence DS.

For a start, the DS looked extraordinary. At the front, the nose sloped to a point. Where was the air intake? At the back, the bodywork curved down to the bumpers and enclosed the rear wheels. The steering wheel had a single spoke.

Then there was the suspension, each wheel being supported independently. The system was self-levelling, with pneumatic struts riding in oil, fed from a central reservoir. When the engine was started, the suspension would gently pump itself up to the correct height, no matter what weight was being carried.

Other marvels included power-assisted steering, power brakes operated by a tiny button on the floor, and an automatic pneumatic clutch. It was a futuristic car, which demanded futuristic drivers, and proved quite a handful for lesser mortals.

MMU 221K
MMU 221K

DC01

1993 James Dyson

In 1998 Tony Blair announced that the DC02 cleaner had been chosen as one of the UK's first 'Millennium' products.

Dyson sponsored Sir Ranulph Fiennes' 1996 Solo Antarctica Expedition.

The inspiration for a bagless cleaner burst into James Dyson's head as he was renovating his house in the Cotswolds. Exasperated by the weak suction of the conventional vacuum cleaner, he identified its weakness as the throwaway bag. The suction passed through this bag: therefore, as soon as the bag began to fill with dust, its pores clogged and the passage of air became blocked.

Between 1979 and 1984 he experimented ceaselessly, building more than 5,000 prototypes for a cleaner which needed no bag. Gradually, he perfected his 'dual cyclone' system, with its greatly increased vacuum power. The first commercial model, called the G-Force and boldly cased in pink, was a huge success worldwide.

But it was the appearance of the Dyson DC01 in May 1993 which captured public imagination. With its see-through panel, elegant lines and startling efficiency, the DC01 was clearly a revolutionary object. Today, it outsells its nearest competitor by nine to one.

The DC01 outsells its nearest competitor by nine to one!

Challenge of Materials Bridge

1995 Chris Wilkinson Architects

Among other Wilkinson-designed bridges are the Hulme Arch in Manchester, The Butterfly Bridge in Bedford and the South Quay Footbridge at Canary Wharf, London.

The most extraordinary addition to London's Science Museum in the 1990s has been the Challenge of Materials Gallery.

A series of stunning architectural conceits creates a framework which allows the visitor to explore the infinite possibilities of material science.

At the heart of the gallery is Chris Wilkinson's magical and intriguing bridge. It spans the atrium, floating at mezzanine level across the internal space and providing a visual focus for the other exhibits. It also demonstrates how materials can be pushed to surprising limits.

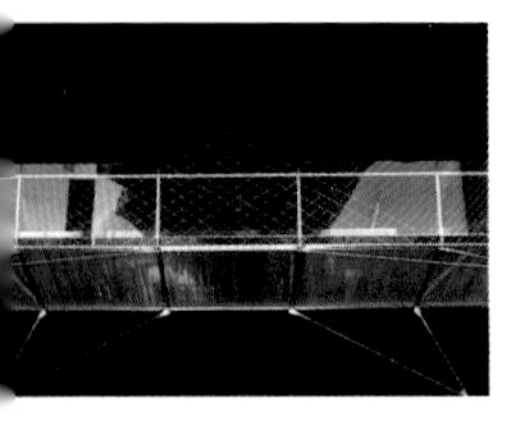

The design of the bridge is simple in the extreme. The deck is formed by over 800 glass planks, suspended from a network of ultra-thin stainless steel wires. Channelled through stress gauges, these wires activate acoustic and lighting systems devised by eccentric sound artist Ron Geesin.

Sony Walkman

1979 Sony Corporation

The name 'Sony' is derived from the Latin *sonus* meaning sound.

Originally, this Japanese corporation had the much more cumbersome title of the Tokyo Tsushin Kogyo Company.

First came the Sony Pressman of 1977, a superlight cassette recorder. Then some bright spark suggested taking away the recording function and adding stereo sound and headphones. Hey presto – the Sony Walkman: indispensable fashion accessory for young strollers, joggers, commuters, shoppers and even swimmers.

But the secret of the Walkman's phenomenal success was far more profound than mere trendiness. For the first time, people could select and carry round with them what one sociologist called 'the inner landscape of sound'. They could dramatise daily life with their own private film soundtrack.

By 1995, over 150 million of them had been sold in a myriad of designs, and now played CDs, Mini-Discs or cassettes. There was a Walkman haircut, a Walkman animated film and a solar-powered Walkman. The personal sound system had conquered the world.

1979

1985

Like Hoover and JCB, Walkman has become a generic term.

1990

1999

Lotus Olympic Pursuit Bike

1992 Lotus

The unheard of efficiency and improved performance of the 108 spooked international cycling authorities so badly, that they initially banned the design.

Eight replicas of Boardman's bike were later built and offered for sale at £15,000 each.

In July 1992, British cyclist Chris Boardman hurtled to a gold medal in the 4000-metre pursuit at the Barcelona Olympics. As well as passing his opponent (an outstanding feat in itself), he broke the world record. A month later, he added the 5000-metre record to his haul.

Boardman was mounted on an eerily beautiful and futuristic-looking machine called the Lotus Sport Bicycle Type 108. Developed and tested in secret, it had been designed to minimise aerodynamic drag on both bike and rider. The key to its success was its aerofoil-section composite monocoque (in layman's terms, the one-piece frame), moulded from a range of advanced materials, notably carbon fibre.

Only 12 models of this breathtaking bike were ever built. But Boardman's success prompted Lotus to develop the idea further. The even more sophisticated Type 110 made a triumphant debut in the 1994 Tour de France.

LOTUS
Sport
MAVIC
3G
MAVIC
3G
MAVIC
3G

Bookworm Bookcase

1993 Ron Arad

Geared towards the mass market, the plastic variant is an affordable design classic! Thus, these vast, looping structures can be found on the walls of book-hoarding octogenarians and students alike.

In 1963, Israeli-born Arad co-founded the Archigram Group in London. It was dedicated to what it called 'architectural deconstructivity', and Arad developed into a leader of the subversive school of design (which was later to have links with punk culture).

His creations consistently surprised and delighted, with their combination of puckish whimsy and harsh realism. These included the Transformer chair – a bag full of polystyrene beads from which a vacuum cleaner sucked air so that it hardened to the sitter's shape.

Ron Arad is currently the Professor of Design Products at the Royal College of Art, London.

The continuous Bookworm bookcase of 1993 has proved daring, popular and practical. Made of blackened tempered steel or flexible translucent plastic, it snaked across walls in whatever loops and curves the buyer fancied. The form is retained by randomly-placed 'fake' books, which double as box brackets.

Gaggia Espresso Machine

1938 Achille Gaggia

Cliff Richard's early film *Expresso Bongo* (1960) was one of many at the time centred on coffee bar culture – in this case, London's Soho.

The first Gaggia machines were imported into the UK by an emigrant Italian dental mechanic who was appalled at the quality of English coffee.

Few inventions have spawned an entire subculture. One such rarity is the espresso coffee machine developed by an indefatigable Italian engineer, Achille Gaggia, in the 1930s. In the post-war years, these gloriously dramatic chrome and gold constructions sold throughout Europe as fast as the Milan factory could make them.

The secret of Gaggia's success lay in the sprung piston system, by which hot water was forced at high pressure through finely ground coffee beans held in a filter. This did away with the traditional need for steam, which produced a much inferior brew.

Modernistic coffee bars sprang up at railway stations and street corners, catering for the new custom of taking a nip of concentrated black coffee at regular intervals throughout the day. These bars became social centres, especially for the young. Dozens of variations were dreamed up – 'cappuccino', 'ristretto' (extra strong) and 'corretto' (with a shot of grappa).

GAGGIA
CREMA CAFFE NATURALE
FUNZIONA SENZA VAPORE

B306 Chaise Longue

1928-29 Le Corbusier/Pierre Jeanneret/Charlotte Perriand

Le Corbusier is regarded primarily as an architect, yet his furniture design partnership with Charlotte Perriand was long-lived and highly influential.

The upholstered parts of the chaise are available in hairy skin, leather or canvas.

Charles Edouard Jeanneret, otherwise Le Corbusier, famously stated that a house was a machine for living in. He extended this to cover the furniture inside as well, and was later to describe his celebrated chaise longue as 'a real machine for rest'.

History has proved him right, both technically and artistically. The B306 is still recommended by orthopedists today as ideal for back sufferers. It does not try to imitate the shape of the body, yet supports the entire back while placing the legs at the correct angle to relieve stress.

The chaise longue is just as pleasing aesthetically. It sits inside another metal frame, which enables it to slide in an arc and thus move the sitter in one smooth continuum from upright to supine. The simple, fluid outlines testify to Le Corbusier's determination to link artistic theory with practice.

Rotring Engineering Pencil

1977 Rotring Group

The invention of the Rotring engineering pencil posed a serious threat to the pencil-sharpening business.

Anzeigenmotiv, 1967

Rotring's ditty (above) advertising the four-colour ballpoint translates as 'Saucy chicks, – bright tips'.

Chunky, unpretentious and utterly dependable, Rotring engineering pencils and pens have no serious rival. The simplicity of the pencil's design – plain aluminium, hexagonal in section – somehow exudes quiet authority. And at its top, the thin red ring (in German, 'rotor ring') subtly proclaims its maker.

It was in 1928 that Wilhelm Riepe developed the world's first nibless fountain pen. The innovation was taken a step further by Wilhelm's son, who launched the radiograph – the original technical pen – in 1953.

The firm became Rotring a decade later and has since grown into a massive worldwide group of companies. Its products now include everything, from capillary ink cartridges and computer-controlled lettering machines to artists' oils and colour cosmetics. But, to a host of planners, designers, inventors and dreamers, the engineering pencil remains its finest contribution to the twentieth century.

Design Museum London

1987-89 Conran/Roche

The museum also houses a resource centre, to service the design industry, as well as Conran's celebrated Blueprint Café.

Terence Conran and Stephen Bayley established the Design Museum to explain, improve and raise awareness of design standards in the UK. They believed that consumer goods deserved a focal point, where their function, appearance and marketing could be examined and explained.

The pair found a disused warehouse overlooking the River Thames near Butler's Wharf. It was too costly to renovate completely, so they decided to demolish and rebuild a major portion. The result was a 'new' 1930s building, an assemblage of rectangles with a subtly layered frontage.

The coolness of the exterior (the original brick having been covered in white stucco) was echoed inside. The galleries on the top two floors are flooded with natural light, bringing to life the neutral tones of oak and marble floors and white walls. The sight of the Thames running smoothly below adds to the general calmness. No wonder one critic praised the Museum's 'atmosphere of quiet decorum'.

DESIGN MUSEUM

Geodesic Dome

1954 R. Buckminster Fuller

Within 30 years of Fuller's patenting his geodesic dome, more than 50,000 structures had been built.

The most well known dome is Disneys' Epcot Centre in Florida, often mistaken for a giant golf ball!

Richard Buckminster Fuller was a brilliant and prophetic engineer, who aimed his many inventions unequivocally at the betterment of humanity. Among these were a rechargeable electric car, a vehicle which could move in any direction and an all-metal house in kit form.

Fuller was intense in his belief that people could control large parts of their environment without being divorced from nature. To that end he developed what he called the 'geodesic' dome. This was a large, lightweight enclosure which combined great strength with a minimal structure.

The surface of the dome is honeycombed into triangular pieces by a latticework of rods. This highly efficient framework can easily support a weather-proof covering. Alternatively, the dome can be formed of solid panels. The geometry of the structure makes it perfectly rigid even when built of a weak material such as cardboard.

RB211 Engine

1968 Rolls-Royce

After the 1971 bankruptcy, Rolls-Royce was re-formed as two separate companies – one to build jet engines, the other to produce automobile and diesel engines.

RB stands for Rolls-Royce Barnoldswick. This division of the legendary company was opened in an old tank engine factory in Nottinghamshire in 1943, and it was here that engineers created many of the most powerful aero engines in the world.

Among these was the RB211, introduced with a flourish in 1968. This pioneering engine, with 40,600lb of thrust, was ordered by Lockheed to power its brand new Tristar airbus. The most astonishing quality of the RB211 was its light weight, thanks to fan blades made of carbon fibre.

The triumph, alas, soon turned to disaster. The revolutionary new carbon material proved too weak for the stresses of wear, and had to be replaced with heavier titanium. Rolls-Royce itself went bankrupt in 1971. But the RB211 was saved. Completely redesigned, it did indeed launch the popular Tristar. And in 1981 Boeing selected an improved model to power the outstandingly efficient 757 airliner – the first time Boeing had ever introduced an aircraft with a non-US power plant.

John Hancock Center Chicago

1968-70 Bruce Graham

The sky lobby – between floors 44-45 – is where everyone changes elevators. You can stop here to eat, shop or even take a dip in the swimming pool.

As American skyscrapers grew taller in the post-war era, materials and design solutions were stretched to the limit. Existing structural systems had to be revised. Added strength and resilience had to be found from somewhere.

The John Hancock Center in Chicago presented a clear answer to the problem. The building's designer Bruce Graham described it succinctly as 'a diagonally braced tube'. The X-shaped bracing on the exterior was a visible expression of its structural efficiency, with the walls bearing most of the vertical load, and also coping with the lateral forces of wind. A secondary system of floors and window panels added sturdiness internally.

The Center is also visually breathtaking, its tapered steel form making a dramatic silhouette against the Chicago skyline. This elegance is heightened by the understated dark colouring of the exterior.

Wink Chair

1980 Toshiyuki Kita

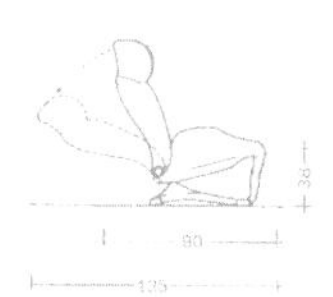

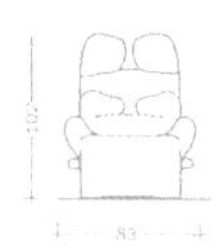

What is an 'animated' chair? The idea of an assemblage of steel, dacron and foam plastic coming to life is perverse. And yet the Wink chair, with its Mickey-Mouse-ear armrests, its rounded contours and its jolly colours, has an animal-like charm quite unlike most other modern furniture. One critic likened it to a gigantic friendly insect.

The Wink moves, too. It can be flexed and bent to many different positions, from upright armchair to lounger. This neatly encapsulates the Japanese custom of sitting on the floor whilst offering the Western visitor the comfort of a traditional backed chair.

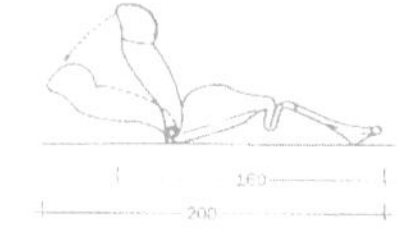

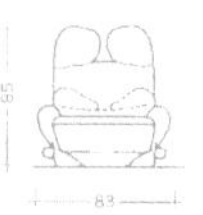

Indeed, the Wink is the embodiment of Toshiyuki's determination to assert his cultural identity. His work, which includes paper lampshades and lacquer tableware, has been instrumental in the recent revival of native Japanese arts. Yet his experiences of the West have led him, he writes, 'to design objects which take into account the values of both worlds'.

Heron Parigi Drawing Board

1964 Paolo Parigi

'Metal is not cold. Metal is beauty, severe and uncompromising. It seeks no accord from the world which surrounds it. It is sublime, of a harshness that needs no sculpting.'
Paolo Parigi

Born near Florence in Italy in 1936, Paolo Parigi found himself learning his trade at the epicentre of post-war innovation in industrial design. At twenty-eight, he unveiled his first mass-produced project, the 'Heron' drawing table, so-called because of its long legs and expectant attitude.

It was an immediate success, and inspired in turn the company name, Heron Parigi. As partner and design director, Parigi has pioneered many ground-breaking products including some astonishing perforated metal benches and office chairs.

The great virtues of his group's designs lie in their apparent simplicity, their use of the minimum of parts and their pride in fine workmanship. These qualities can be seen to best effect in their vast range of drawing boards and tables, with their robust mechanisms and graceful efficiency.

Chrysler Building New York

1928-30 William van Alen

The Chrysler Building's interior is no less spectacular, but the ever present threat of terrorism ensures that only a minority are witness to the glorious art deco lobby, lifts and stairways.

The first American skyscrapers in 1880s Chicago were of simple and unpretentious design which followed the logic of the framework. When the fashion reached New York, architects began to give imagination its head. Their skyscrapers grew into soaring, sculpted and ornamented fantasies, which reflected the confident pride of a brash young country.

The Chrysler Building is the culmination of this style. Designed by William van Alen, it celebrated the commercial triumph of the Chrysler Corporation by being (for a few months) the world's tallest building.

It is also one of the most flamboyant. On a 20-storey base of silver-grey brick stands a massive middle section, rearing up from which is the tapering spire. Scalloped windows,sunburst panels, giant metal Chrysler radiator caps and colossal American eagles adorn this upper part, making it unmistakeably a 'Cathedral of Capitalism'.

Austin Morris Mini

1959 Alex Issigonis

The Mini achieved its apotheosis with starring roles in '60s heist movies, *The Italian Job* (1969) and *The Thomas Crown Affair* (1968). Lawrence, the unfortunate husband of Beverly, in *Abigail's Party* (1977), upgraded his Mini every year.

It began life as the BMC 850 and became the Austin Seven – the fifth car to bear that proud name. But it achieved legendary, almost totemic, status as the Mini, the most successful small car ever made. Sir Alex Issigonis had already designed one classic 'compact', the Morris Minor, when he became BMC's chief engineer in 1951. Soon he landed an even more challenging brief: to create a car which was small, fuel efficient and revolutionary in shape.

The result was an astonishing landmark in automobile design, launched in 1959. With its engine set transversely and its gearbox nestling down in the sump, the new car was less than ten feet long. Yet it could easily carry four people and, thanks to small wheels and independent rubber suspension, it gave them a comfortable ride.

One major stimulus for the creation of the economical Mini was the Suez Crisis of 1956, which had led to petrol rationing.

Above all, the Mini was perfectly suited to the spirit of the times. Cheeky, unconventional and nippy (with excellent road-holding qualities, thanks to front-wheel drive), it was embraced as a chic symbol of the Swinging Sixties. With over six million sold, it has never gone out of fashion.

DRM 383C

Rietveld Chair

1917 Gerrit Rietveld

Later versions of the chair were finished in polychromic paint or black stain, actually making it red, blue and black.

Rietveld was peculiarly suited to spearheading the revolution in furniture and interior design in the early years of the twentieth century. Following in his father's footsteps, he had trained as a cabinet-maker, all the while studying architecture at night school.

This background, allied to the new theories of geometric abstraction promoted by the De Stijl group, led Rietveld to view furniture as something which could define space. In 1917 he designed and made the famous red/blue chair in his own workshop. He built it of bare wood (with side panels which were later removed).

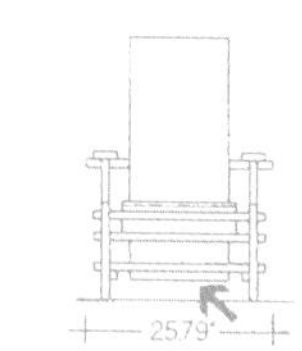

His aim was to produce something which was not only an exercise in design, but also a piece of fine art, and he tried to lay aside all preconceptions of how a chair might look. Nonetheless, the result was perfectly comfortable and functional as a piece of furniture. What's more, it could easily be constructed by any craftsman cabinetmaker.

JCB Digger

1953 Joseph Bamford

Bamford insisted that all his diggers were fitted with electric kettles. That way, the operator wouldn't have to leave the comfort of his cab for a tea break.

Before 1953 no-one had ever dug a ditch without a hand shovel. Then came Joe Bamford's Mark I Hydraulic Excavator. It fitted on a standard Fordson tractor, could swivel a full 180 degrees and dig up to 45 cubic yards per hour. Above all, it made use of the incredible force which could be generated by hydraulic power.

Over the next half century, JCBs played a major part in transforming the face of Britain – and the rest of the world. They sprouted bulldozer blades, backhoe buckets and crawler tracks. They became a permanent fixture on building and motorway sites, farms and quarries.

'JCB' even gained the rare distinction of becoming a generic word, a shorthand description for all excavators. Indeed, it now has its own proud entry in the Oxford English Dictionary.

Bamford's secret for success? 'I always count the number of parts: parts are money. Better to keep it simple.'

INDUSTRIAL MAJOR LOADER

Another  *Product*

J.C. BAMFORD

LAKESIDE WORKS · ROCESTER · UTTOXETER · STAFFS · ENG

(Our only address — No connection with any other firm)

Telephone : ROCESTER 371/2 Telegrams : LAKESIDE, ROCESTER

Eames Lounge Chair

1956 Charles and Ray Eames

Charles and Ray Eames were also experimental filmmakers, and featured their chair in an animated short. The title, naturally, was *Eames Lounge Chair.*

One common misconception is that this was the chair designed for film director, Billy Wilder; that was the Eames chaise longue.

'The warm receptive look of a well-used first baseman's mitt.' This was the homely aim of Charles and Ray Eames when they created their Lounge Chair – and a homely object it has become, reproduced in a thousand guises all over the world. Derided by some as too conventional, and even too ugly, it is still a bestseller.

In the 1950s, the Eames design partnership had accepted the challenge to design a modern American equivalent of the comfortable leather armchair beloved of English gentleman's clubs. The result had to be culturally acceptable to a wide range of people.

The chair's basic framework was of three pieces of plywood, moulded in no more than two planes. This was covered in rosewood veneer and button black leather upholstery, stuffed with down, feather and foam. The whole rotated on an ingenious 'spider' mechanism.

Toio Lamp

1962 Achille and Pier Giacomo Castiglioni

The floor lamps in Castiglioni's oeuvre are among the most beautiful and simple of his designs. His Toio lamp, and the Parentesi, a lamp suspended between floor and ceiling, are featured in the Museum of Modern Art's collection in New York.

With his brother Pier Giacomo, Achille Castiglioni emerged as a major driving force behind modern Italian design after the Second World War. Together they re-thought form, function and manufacturing techniques, and produced work of apparently effortless grace and practicality.

For many of Castiglioni's most enduring designs, he made use of many 'off-the-shelf' items, employing ready-made technology in fresh and often surprising ways. A tractor seat was fixed on a steel support to create a chair. The business end of the Toio floor lamp was simply a car headlamp.

The headlamp, directed upwards, was mounted on an adjustable-height brass stem which was nickel-plated and polished. The chunky rectangular base was of enamelled steel. The novelty, as Castiglioni pointed out, lay not in the way the lamp looked but in the way it was put together.

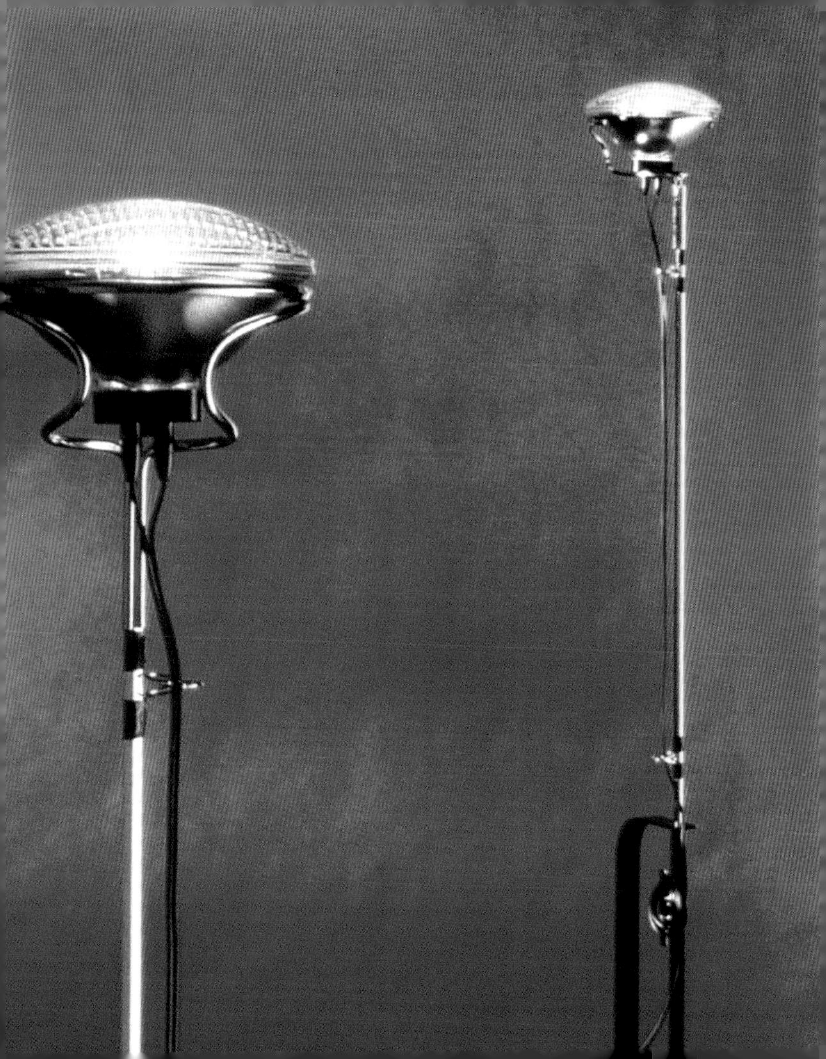

Volkswagen Beetle

1936 Ferdinand Porsche

The VW Beetle is remarkably seaworthy. In 1974 a model – specially sealed and fitted with a propeller – crossed the Irish Sea in seven and a half hours.

The New Beetle was unveiled in 1999 complete with styling and technology for tomorrow's world, right down to the dashboard mounted vase and flower.

The engine was in the boot and made a quite unmistakable ticking noise, like a sewing machine. It hardly seemed to use any petrol at all. Shopping and luggage went under the bonnet. The interior was spartan. The body profile was sturdy and starkly aerodynamic.

The Volkswagen 'Beetle' not only outsold all other cars worldwide, but did so over an extraordinary length of time. It was originally devised as an economical 'People's Car' (or 'Strength Through Joy Car') for the denizens of Nazi Germany, to be assembled by a co-operative group of factories. Plans for mass production were halted when war broke out in 1939.

Work resumed in 1945, and by 1950 over 80,000 VWs a year were hitting the roads. Within two decades, annual output was well over one million, and the Beetle soon overhauled the Model T Ford as the most popular automobile ever. Amazingly enough, for such an ancient and workaday object, it still holds its place in the public affections.

J8 VWW

Picture Credits

Every possible effort has been made to attribute all photographic credits as accurately as possible. In the instance of any mistakes or omissions, Absolute Press would like to offer their apologies and ask that misrepresented parties bring any such errors to our attention.

14 & 15 Courtesy of Luceplan SPA
17 © Jeremy Flack/Aviation Photographs International
19 © Hovercraft Museum Trust (http://www.hovercraft-museum.org)
20 & 21 © Martyn Goddard
23 © Dyson
24 & 25 © James Morris / Courtesy of Chris Wilkinson Architects Limited.
Project consultants: Whitby Bird & Partners; Hubbard Architectural Metalwork Limited; Ron Geesin
27 © Sony
28 & 29 © Lotus
31 © Ron Arad Associates Limited
33 © Gaggia (with thanks to Justin Stockwell, Chevron Foods Limited)
34 & 35 Courtesy of Cassina USA
36 & 37 © Rotring / Courtesy of Sanford UK
38 & 39 © Jefferson Smith / Courtesy of Design Museum
41 © Richard Bryant / Courtesy of Arcaid
42 & 43 © Rolls-Royce plc
44 & 45 © Ezra Stoller/Esto/Arcaid / Courtesy of Arcaid
46 & 47 Courtesy of Cassina USA
48 & 49 © Heron Parigi
51 © David Churchill/Arcaid / Courtesy of Arcaid
53 © Hulton Getty
54 & 55 Courtesy of Cassina USA
56 & 57 © JCB
59 © Eames Office (http://www.eamesoffice.com)
61 Courtesy of Flos USA
63 © Volkswagen

Front cover: © Ron Arad Associates Limited
Back cover left: © Jefferson Smith / Courtesy of Design Museum
Back cover right: Courtesy of Flos USA